They live in a bejeweled palace in Zahramay Falls.

This is Shimmer!

This is Shine!

Nahal is Shine's feisty little tiger cub.

Let's Draw!

Use the grid to draw Nahal.

Tala is Shimmer's playful little monkey.

Tic-Tac-Toe

Nahal is the purr-fect pet!

Tala loves to climb.

A-Maze-ing!

Help Shine find Nahal.

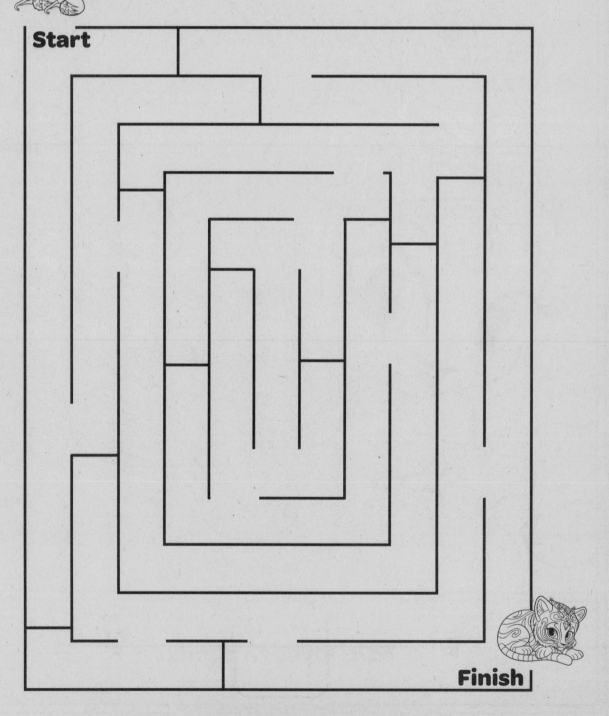

Start

Finish

Which is Different?

Which Tala is different from the others?

A

B

C

D

Your Answer:

Just like the genies . . .

. . . Tala and Nahal make a great team!

A Dazzling Duo

How Many?

How many jewels do you see?

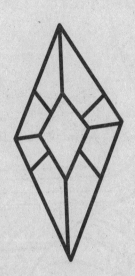

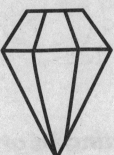

Your Answer:

Shimmer loves glitter and giving hugs.

Shine loves telling silly jokes.

Another beautiful day in Zahramay Falls!

The two genies play with their pets.

Tic-Tac-Toe

Let's Draw!

Use the grid to draw Tala.

Shadow Match

Which shadow matches Nahal?

A

B

C

When Leah needs help, she calls for her genies.

**Shimmer and Shine grant
Leah three wishes a day!**

How Many?

How many genie bottles do you see?

Your Answer:

Design Your Own Hanging Lamps.

Who's a cute little monkey?

Which is Different?

Which image is different from the others?

A   B

C   D

Your Answer:

Zac is Leah's friend and neighbor.

Shadow Match

Which shadow matches Shimmer?

A

B

C

Shimmer and Shine get a call from Leah.

Genies to the rescue!

Which is Different?

Which Shine is different from the others?

A

B

C

D

Your Answer:

Shimmer and Shine do their best,
but the wishes don't always come out as planned.

Double Trouble!

Shadow Match

Which shadow matches Leah?

A

B

C

Magical Misadventures

Tala and Nahal

A-Maze-ing!

Help Shimmer and Shine get to Leah.

Start

Finish

You're a gem!

**When things go wrong,
Leah and the dazzling duo always find a way.**

They work together to save the day!

How Many?

How many hearts do you see?

Your Answer:

Make it shimmer!

Make it shine!

Let's Draw!

Use the grid to draw Shimmer.

Boom Zahramay!

Magic Moves

Tic-Tac-Toe

Sweet and Sparkly

How Many?

How many pillows do you see?

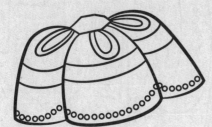

Your Answer:

It's MAGIC!

A-Maze-ing!

Help Shimmer find Shine.

Start

Finish

Shine On!

Wish Granted!

Shadow Match

Which shadow matches Shine?

A

B

C

Tic-Tac-Toe

Sweet Monkey

I'm the cat's MEOW!

Shine

Which is Different?

Which Shimmer is different from the others?

A

B

C

D

Your Answer:

Let's Draw!

Use the grid to draw Leah.

Design Your Own Genie Bottle.

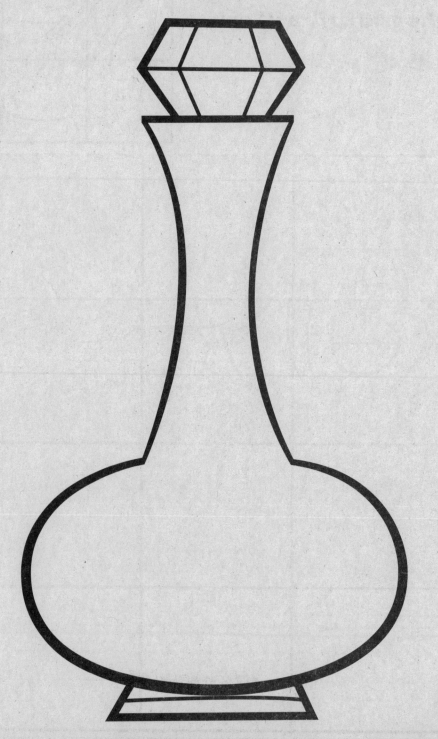

It's magic!

A-Maze-ing!

Help Shimmer and Shine find their pets.

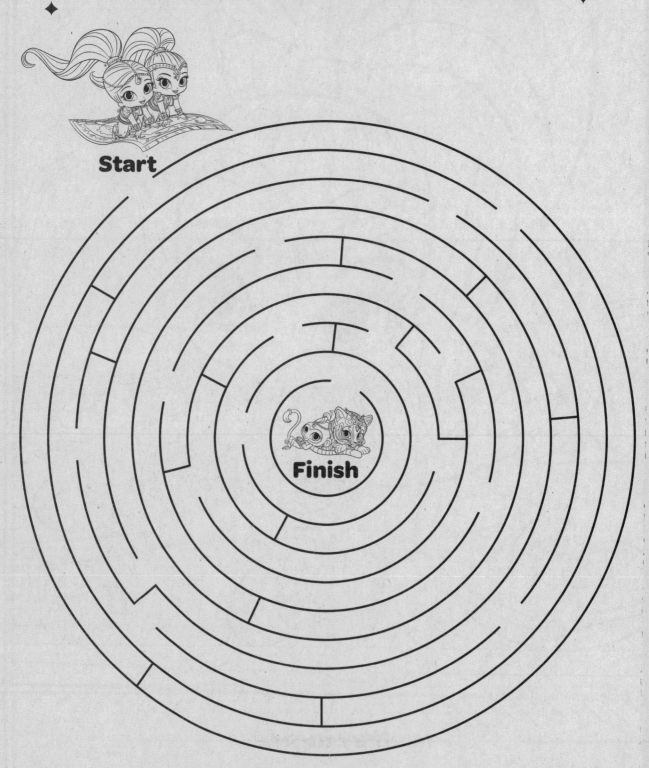

Start

Finish

Monkey Business

Glitter Friends

Let's Draw!

Use the grid to draw Shine.

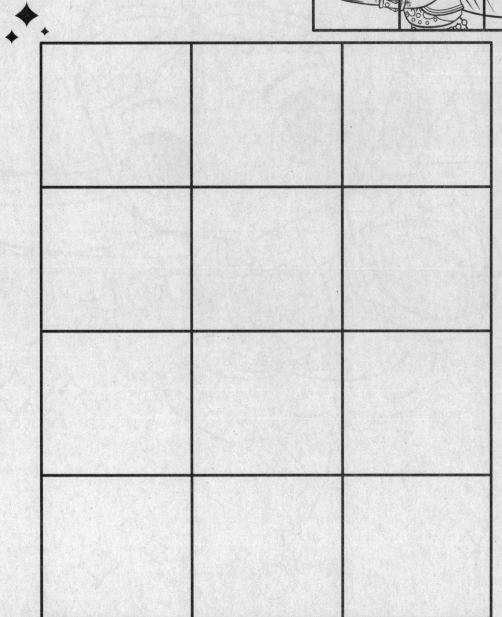

Which is Different?

Which Zac is different from the others?

A

B

C

D

Your Answer:

I love Nahal!

Tic-Tac-Toe

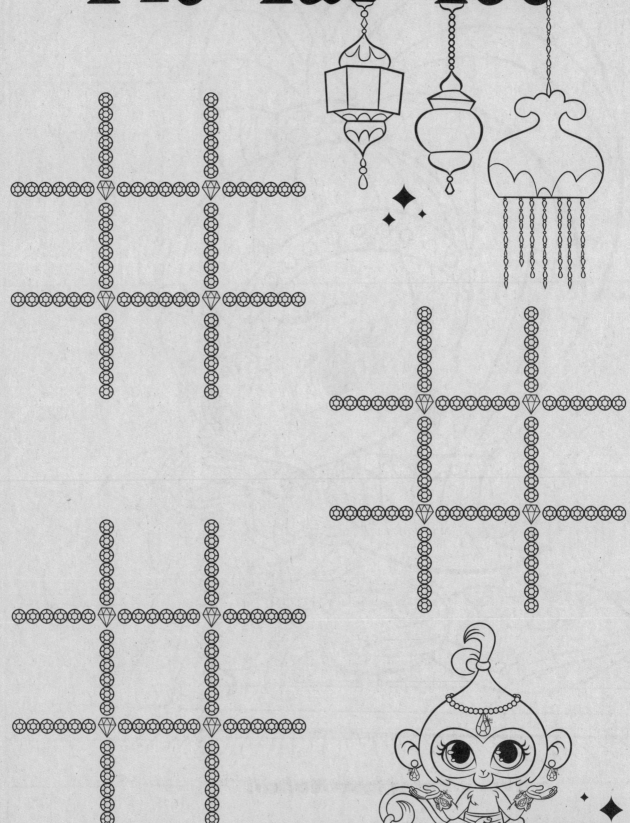

Everyone could use a little glitter!

Design Your Own Magic Carpet.

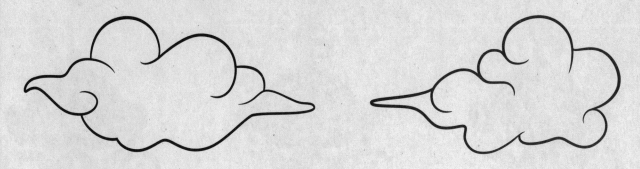

Shadow Match

Which shadow matches Tala?

A   B   C

A-Maze-ing!

Help Nahal find her bowl.

Start

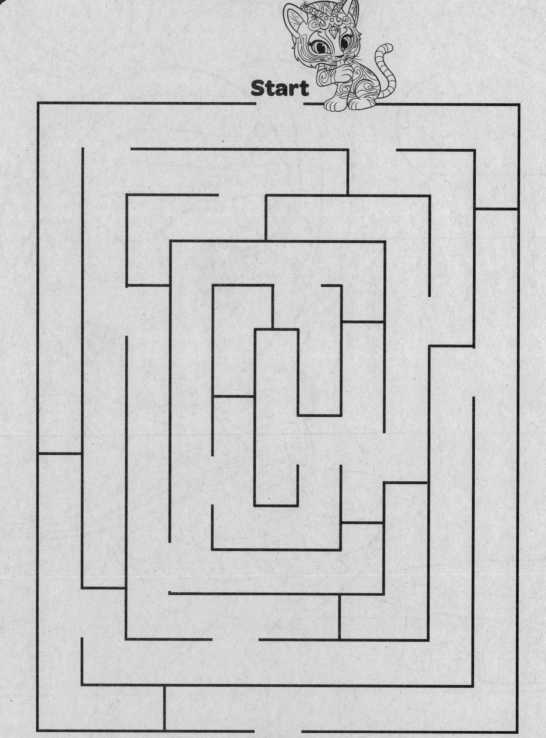

Finish

How Many?

How many lamps do you see?

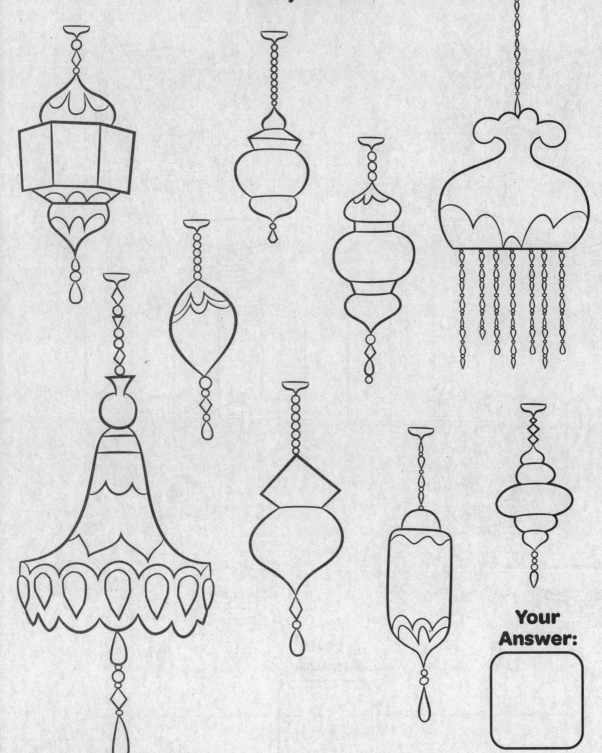

Your Answer:

Which is Different?

Which Nahal is different from the others?

A

B

C

D

Your Answer:

You had me at MEOW!

Which is Different?

Which image is different from the others?

A

B

C

D

Your Answer:

Design Shine's bedroom.

What's your wish?

We did it!
¡Lo hicimos!

We better watch
out for Swiper.

Draw lines to connect the pictures that match!

Come on!
¡Vámonos!

Fall Friends! ¡Amigos del Otoño!

What's cooking?
¿Qué está cocinando?

Exploring summer!
¡Explorando el verano!

Help Backpack!
Circle something that Dora can ride on!

Buenos Amigos

If you see a fox, yell "Swiper!"

Backpack and Map

Here we go! ¡Aquí vamos!

A Party!
¡Una Fiesta!

Beach Buddies!
¡Amigos de la playa!

To the rescue!

¡Al rescate!

Find the missing piece of the puzzle!

BENNY

What do los pajaritos say? TWEET, TWEET!

Circle the HAT that does not match the others.

Sing, Baby Bird!

¡Canta, pajarito!

Connect the dots!

Let's Go!
¡Vámonos!

That Sneaky Fox!

Color the pictures below that begin with the letter

p

High Seas Explorers!

¡Exploradores de Alta Mar!

Tico

Squirrel! ¡La ardilla!

Hi!
¡Hola!

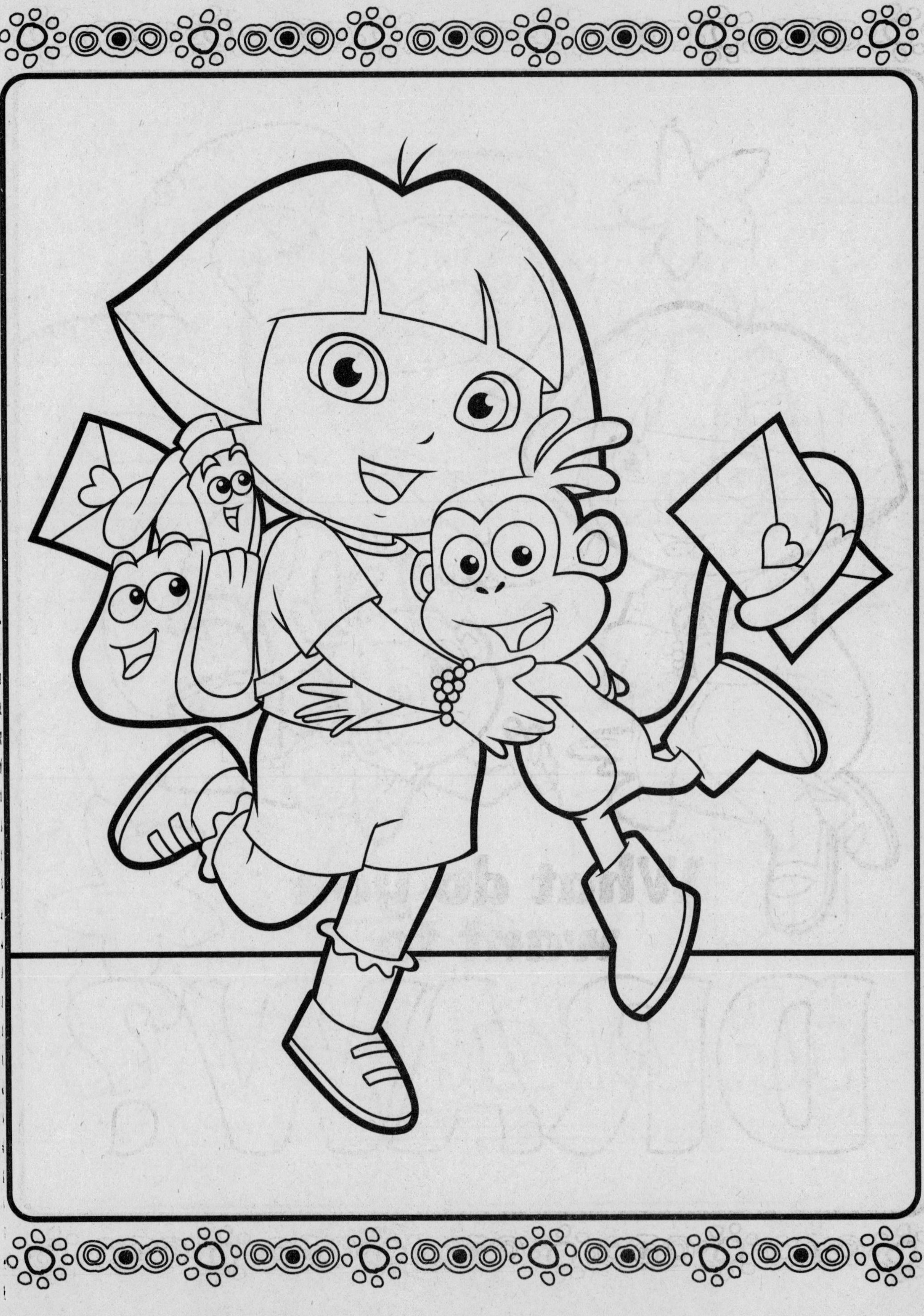

What do you
want to
DRAW?

Swiper

¡Las flores! Flowers!

Find the CIRCLE. ◯ Color it GREEN.

Find the RECTANGLE. ▭ Color it BLUE.

Find the STAR. ☆ Color it PINK.

Find the TRIANGLE. △ Color it RED.

¡Mira las estrellas!

Look at all the stars!

This fruit is fantástica!

Dora, Map and Benny

Let's celebrate!

¡Vamos a celebrar!

You have to say,
"Swiper, no swiping!"

Color all of the LARGE stars.

Connect the dots!

Have an apple, Isa!

Surprise! ¡Sorpresa!

Help Backpack!
Circle something that Dora can read to Boots!

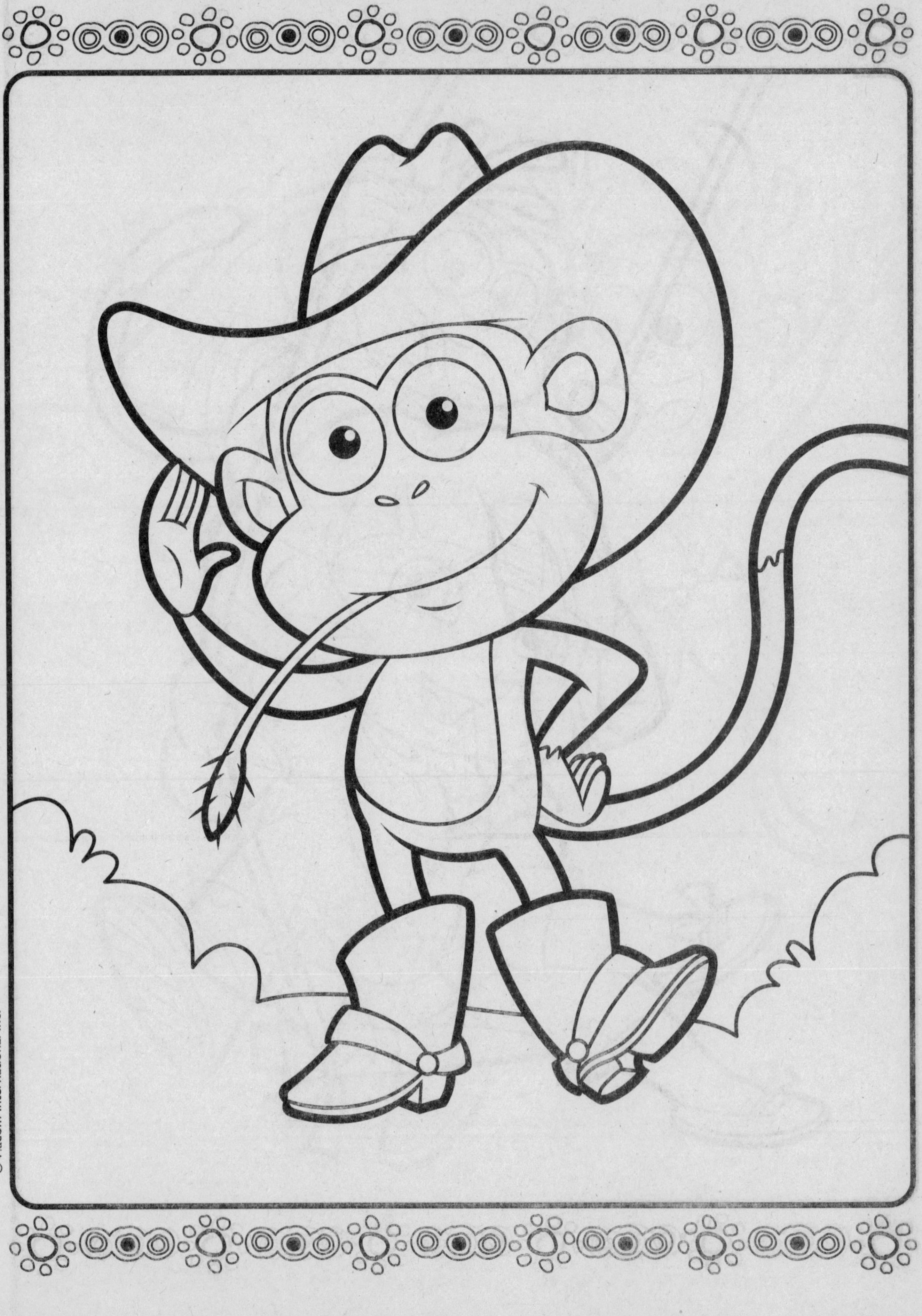

Ready for school!

¡Lista para escuela!

Benny and Tico

Everybody, dance!

Best Friend Moments!

¡Momentos de Buenos Amigos!

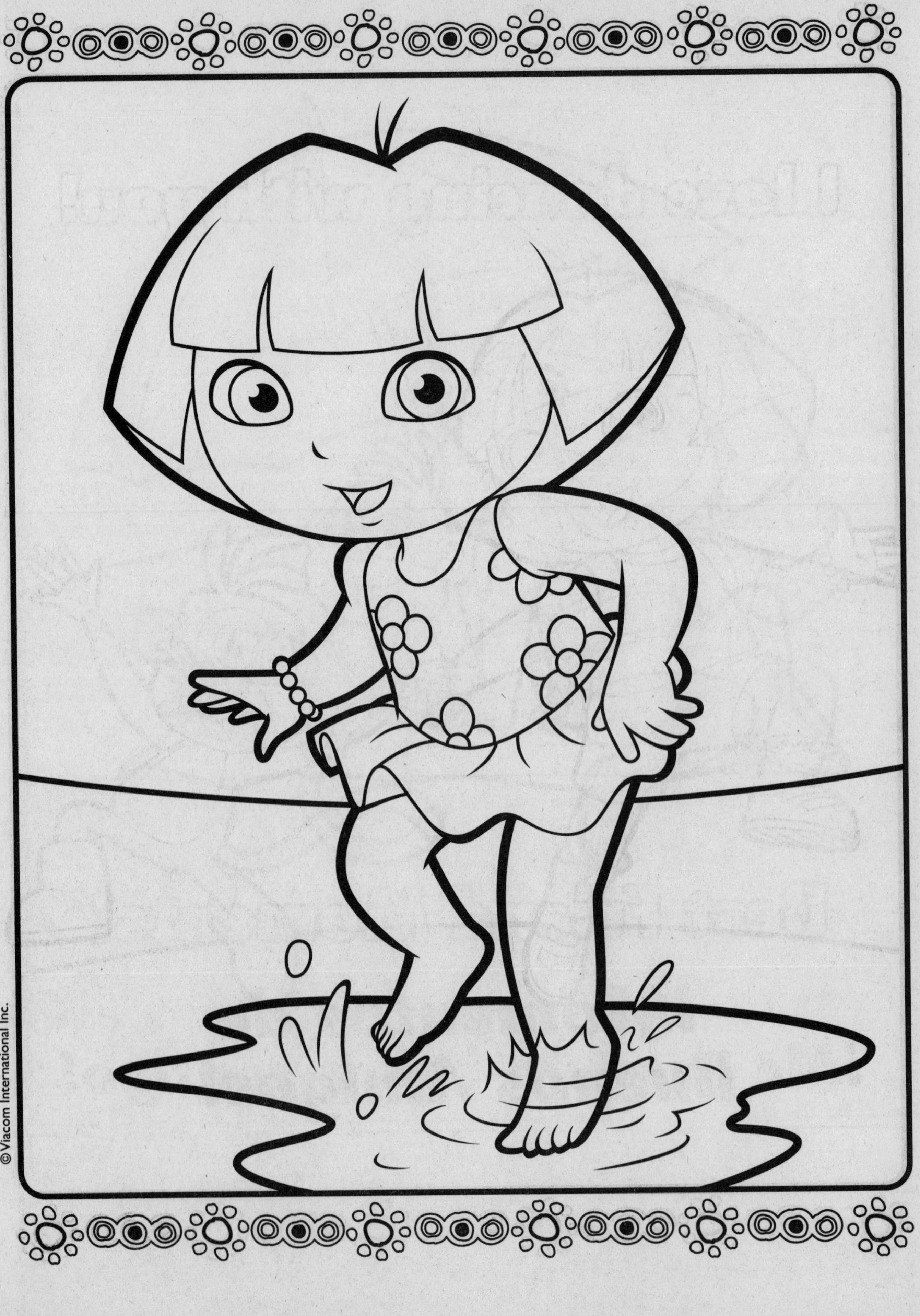

I love dancing with you!

¡Me encanta bailar contigo!

Isa and Boots

Fresh fruits!

¡Frutas frescas!

Benny and Boots

Dora and Boots

Backpack
and Map

Let's Dance!

¡Vamos a bailar!

A beachy
Adventure

¡Muy bien, Tico!

Help Dora and Boots find their way through the maze to catch Swiper.

A Fiesta with Friends!

Best Friends!
¡Buenos amigos!

Count the STARS and color the correct number below.

3 4 5

Fluttering into Adventure

¡Qué mono!

It's a monkey masterpiece!

Jump!
¡Salta!

nickelodeon™

DORA the EXPLORER™

Dora and Friends
JUMBO Coloring & Activity Book

D1097107

NickJr.com

nickelodeon™

BENDON™

Bendon Publishing International, Inc.
Ashland, OH 44805
www.bendonpub.com